by ANN TOMPERT

illustrated by ELFREDA

A WHITMAN BOOK
Western Publishing Company, Inc.
Racine, Wisconsin

What makes my cat purr?
What starts that motor she has inside?
Is it the dish of warm milk I give her to drink . . .

the catnip mouse she bats and tosses
into the air . . .

the lap she curls up in . . .

or father's favorite chair?

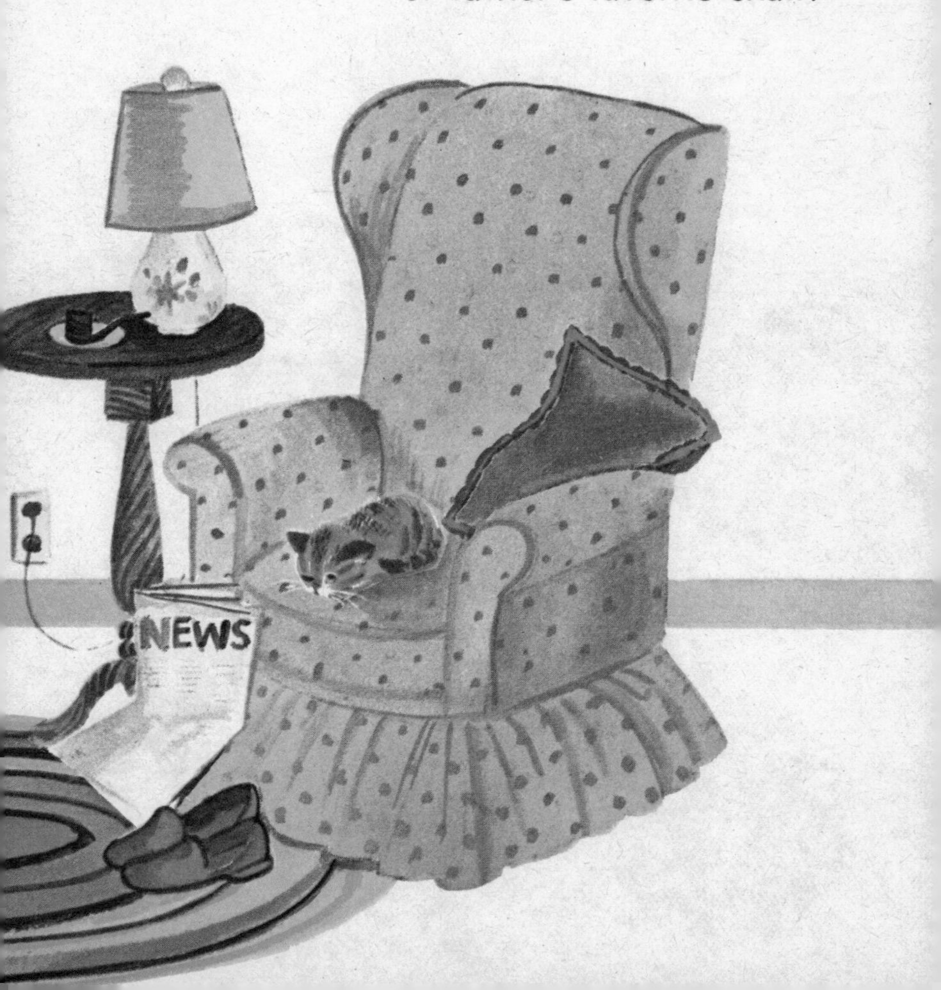

Does she purr because she has a ball of yarn to tangle . . .

a pencil to roll . .

or paper to tear into a million shreds?

Is it because she can wash in a patch of sun-
light on the living room rug . . .

or sleep s-t-r-e-t-c-h-e-d out
along the top of the garden wall?

Maybe she purrs
because she has a fence
to sharpen her claws on . . .

flowers to smell, butterflies to chase,

and trees to climb.

Could she purr because she has so many places to hide? Under beds . . .

in boxes . . .

and bags . . .

and bushes.

What makes my cat purr?
Is it watching the goldfish in the bowl . . .

rolling on the soft, green grass . . .

stalking bugs along the brick wall . . .

or pouncing on hands
weeding the garden?

Perhaps my cat purrs because she likes me to gently stroke her whiskers, rub her ears, and brush her back.

Why does my cat purr?

Is it because she knows that she's ever so beautiful . . .

and that I love her?